Kipper was looking at a book. The book was about a dragon. Kipper couldn't read the story.

Biff didn't want to read it. She didn't like dragons.

Kipper went into Chip's room. Chip
read the story.
"I like dragons," said Chip.

Something was glowing. It was the
magic key.
"Oh no!" said Chip.

Chip picked up the box. He ran into
Biff's room.
"The magic is working," he said.

Biff picked up the key. They looked
at the magic house.
"The door is open," said Biff.

The magic was working. It took the
children inside. It took Floppy too.

It took them to a wood.

Floppy didn't like the wood. He was frightened.

Biff pulled Floppy.

"Come on," she said. "Don't be silly."

An owl flew out of a tree. Floppy
didn't like the owl. He ran away.

Floppy ran out of the wood.
"Come back," called Biff.
"Come back," called Chip.

It was no good. Floppy ran and ran.
"Oh help!" said Biff.

The children looked for Floppy. They called and called.

"Floppy! Come back!" they called.

The children came to a tree. It was called "The Dragon Tree". A dragon lived under the tree.

The dragon had Floppy. He wanted
Floppy for supper. Floppy was
frightened.

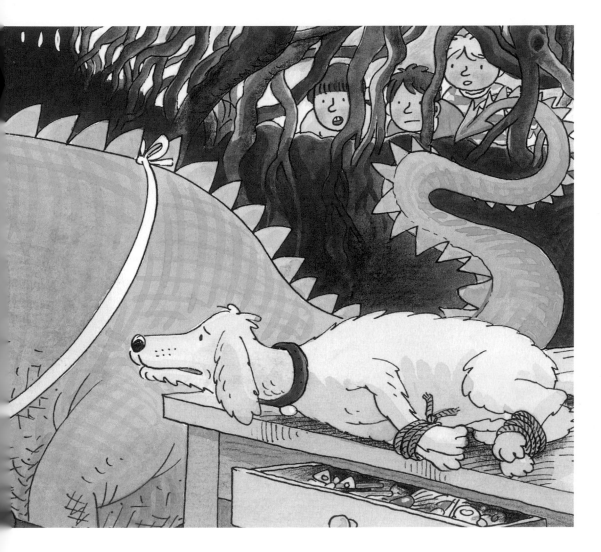

"Oh no!" said Biff. "What a nasty dragon! I don't like dragons!"

Biff looked at the dragon's tail. She
took off her belt.

She put it round the tail. Chip
helped her.

Kipper went inside the tree. He
pulled Floppy out. Chip helped him.

The dragon was cooking. It didn't
see them.

"Come on!" called Chip.
They ran and ran. The key was
glowing.

"The key is glowing," called Biff. "It's time to go home."

"What an adventure!" said Chip.
"I don't like dragons," said Biff.